Acknowledgements
The publishers gratefully acknowledge permission to reproduce copyright material.
Every effort has been made to trace copyright holders, but the publishers would be
interested to hear from any not here acknowledged.
BATES, H.E.: Extracts from *A Love of Flowers,* Michael Joseph, 1971. Reprinted with
permission of Laurence Pollinger Ltd on behalf of the Estate of H.E. Bates. BEARD,
HENRY & MICKIE, ROY: Definitions from *A Gardener's Dictionary.* Reprinted with
permission of Methuen, London and Workman Publishing Company, New York.
CLARKE, ROBIN: Definitions from *The Completely Unillustrated Encyclopaedia of
Gardening.* This first appeared in *New Scientist* magazine, London, the weekly review
of science and technology. FINNIS, VALERIE: Extract from *A Gardener's Dozen*
reprinted with permission of BBC Enterprises Ltd. JENNINGS, PAUL: Extract from
an article first published in *The Observer,* 1 April 1962. KIPLING, RUDYARD:
Extract from *The Glory of the Garden* reprinted with permission of The National Trust.
LEE, LAURIE: Extract from *Cider with Rosie,* reprinted with permission of Chatto &
Windus Ltd. SANSKRIT POEM: From *Poems from the Sanskrit* (Penguin Classics,
1968) © John Brough. Reproduced with permission of Penguin Books Ltd.
TEASDALE, SARA: Extract from 'Night'. Reprinted with permission of Macmillan
Publishing Company from *Collected Poems of Sara Teasdale.* Copyright 1930 by Sara
Teasdale Filsinger, renewed 1958 by Guaranty Trust Co. of New York.
TITCHMARSH, ALAN: Extracts from *The Gardener's Logbook* reprinted with
permission of William Collins Sons & Co. Ltd and Lennard Publishing, WADDELL,
HELEN: 'On Early Morning' from *Lyrics from the Chinese.* Reprinted with permission
of Constable Publishers.

Published simultaneously in 1992 by Exley Publications Ltd in Great
Britain and Exley Giftbooks in the USA.
Copyright © Exley Publications, 1989
Reprinted 1990
Third and fourth printing 1992
Fifth and sixth printings 1993
ISBN 1-85015-119-9

Printed and bound in Spain by Grafo S.A., Bilbao.

Exley Publications Ltd, 16 Chalk Hill, Watford, Herts WD1 4BN, United Kingdom.
Exley Giftbooks, 359 East Main Street, Suite 3D, Mount Kisco, NY 10549, USA.

An illustrated

Gardener's Notebook

illustrated by Juliette Clarke
and edited by Helen Exley

EXLEY
MT. KISCO, NEW YORK · WATFORD, UK

POPPY

POPPY

He who plants a garden, plants happiness.

Chinese proverb

What a man needs in gardening is a cast-iron back with a hinge in it.

Anon.

West-country gardener, looking at row of very stunted broad beans which his employer had sown: 'I'm sorry for your bees, sir, they'll get sore knees sucking 'em.'

I work with nature, not against it, and use only plants that will thrive in my area.

Sir Frederick Gibberd

...a real gardener is not a man who cultivates flowers; he is a man who cultivates the soil.

Karel Capete

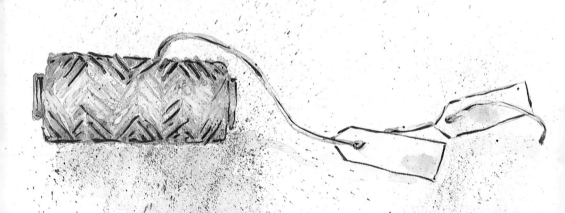

Oh, Adam was a gardener, and God who made him sees
That half a proper gardener's work is done upon his knees.
                                                          Rudyard Kipling

Probably more pest can be controlled in an armchair in front
of a February fire with a garden notebook and a seed
catalogue than can ever be knocked out in hand-to-hand
combat in the garden.
                                                          Neely Turner

And why worry about clothes? Look how the wild flowers grow: they do not work or make clothes for themselves. But I tell you that not even King Solomon with all his wealth had clothes as beautiful as one of these flowers.

From Luke 16.13; 28

Furrow: Horizontal line on forehead of gardener.
Garden: One of a vast number of free outdoor restaurants
operated by charity-minded amateurs in an effort to provide
healthful, balanced meals for insects, birds, and animals.
Hose: Crude, but effective and totally safe, type of scythe
towed through gardens to flatten flower beds and level
vegetable plantings.
Nursery: The only known place where money grows on trees.
Perennial: Any plant which had it lived would have bloomed
year after year.

Henry Beard and Roy McKie
from Gardening: A Gardener's Dictionary

I don't believe the half I hear
        Nor the quarter of what I see!
But I have one faith, sublime and true,
        That nothing can shake or slay;
Each spring I firmly believe anew
        All the seed catalogues say!

Carolyn Wells

Delphinium

Cranesbill

Forget-me-not

Pansy

On Early Morning
    Peach blossom after rain
       Is deeper red;
    The willow fresher green;
       Twittering overhead;
And fallen petals lie wind-blown
Unswept upon the courtyard stone

              Translated from the Chinese
                by Helen Waddell

Far beyond hope the Spring is kind again,
Lovely beyond the longing of my eyes.

Margaret Cropper

There is one luxury item in the utilitarian garden: a potting shed. I've just built one. It's a fabulous haven among composts and flowerpots and forks. As an escape from the family I recommend it with no reservations at all!

Alan Titchmarsh

The works of a person that builds begin immediately to decay; while those of him who plants begin directly to improve. In this, planting promises a more lasting pleasure than building.

William Shenstone

*You fight dandelions all weekend, and late Monday
afternoon there they are, pert as all get out, in full and
gorgeous bloom, pretty as can be, thriving as only dandelions
can in the face of adversity.*

Hal Borland

But a little garden, the littler the better, is your richest chance for happiness and success.

Reginald Farrer

The kiss of the sun for pardon,
    The song of the birds for mirth,
One is nearer God's Heart in a garden
    Than anywhere else on earth.

Dorothy Frances Gurney

Earth laughs in flowers.

Ralph Waldo Emerson

The daisy looks up in my face
As long ago it smiled.
It knows no change but keeps its place
And takes me for a child.

John Clare

In gardening, one's staunchest ally is the natural lust for life each plant has, that strong current which surges through everything that grows.

Jean Hersey

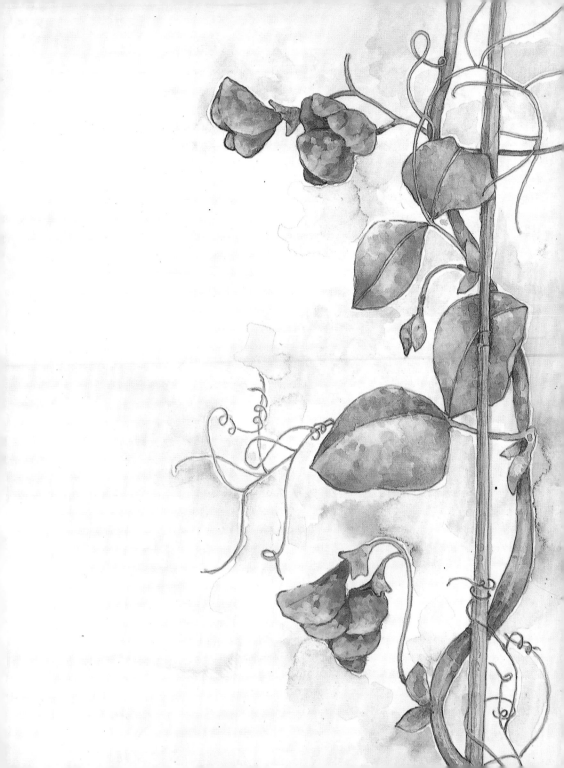

With tumbled hair of swarms of bees,
And flower-robes dancing in the breeze,
With sweet, unsteady lotus-glances,
Intoxicated, Spring advances.

from a Sanskrit poem

One of the great things about gardening is that when the huge wave of summer does finally break, and its leaping curve of green flings into every garden a marvellous iridiscent spray of petals, in colours our language hasn't caught up with yet, its joyful and indiscriminate tide lifts everyone off their feet – both proper gardeners and people like me.

Paul Jennings

from The Green Linnet

Beneath these fruit-tree boughs that shed
Their snow-white blossoms on my head,
With brightest sunshine round me spread
Of spring's unclouded weather,
In this sequestered nook how sweet
To sit upon my orchard-seat!
And birds and flowers once more to greet,
My last year's friends together.

William Wordsworth

A garden makes sure you always have something to worry about.

                                                        Pam Brown

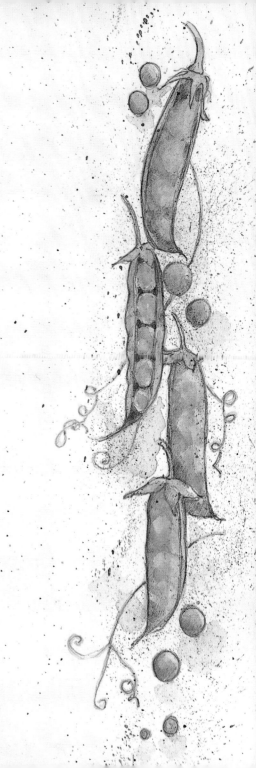

Mother's father had a touch with horses; she had the same with flowers. She could grow them anywhere, at any time, and they seemed to live longer for her. She grew them with rough, almost slap-dash love, but her hands possessed such an understanding of their needs they seemed to turn to her like another sun.

Laurie Lee

Gardening can become a kind of disease. It infects you; you cannot escape it. When you go visiting, your eyes rove about the garden; you interrupt the serious cocktail drinking because of an irrestible impulse to get up and pull a weed.

Lewis Gannit

nigella . · · love in the mist · · ·

nigella

Love in the mist

· nigella · ·)

seeds

seeds from
inside the pod.

Love in the mist · · · Love in the mist · · · nigella · · ·

⟨ Love in the mist - nigella ·

Juliette Clarke 1986

A garden should be in a constant state of fluid change, expansion, experiment, adventure; above all it should be an inquisitive, loving but self-critical journey on the part of its owner.

H.E. Bates

The garden that is finished is dead.

H.E. Bates

Here's flowers for you;
Hot lavender, mints, savory, marjoram;
The marigold that goes to bed with the sun,
And with him rises weeping: these are flowers
Of middle summer, and I think they are given
To men of middle age.

William Shakespeare

The work of a garden bears visible fruits – in a world where most of our labours seem suspiciously meaningless.

Pam Brown

Turnip

Broad Bean

Peas

Onion

Fruit: General term for the seed-bearing part of a plant that is eaten by birds or worms, drops off, rots, gets funny spots, isn't what was pictured in the catalogue, tastes like a glove or doesn't appear at all.

Henry Beard and Roy McKie
from Gardening: A Gardener's Dictionary

For a person whose work throws up an agreed set of figures at the end of each day, a garden is the last sane place on earth.

Pam Brown

Those Latin Names

Who took me by the hand:
Why English flowers had Latin names
She couldn't understand,
Those funny, friendly English flowers,
That bloom from year to year –
She asked me if I would explain
And so I said to her:

Eranthis is an aconite
As everybody knows,
And Helleborous Niger is
Our friend the Christmas rose.
Galanthus is a snowdrop,
Matthiola is a stock,
And Cardamine the meadow flower
Which you call lady's smock.
Muscari is grape hyacinth.
Dianthus is a pink –
And that's as much as one small head
Can carry, I should think.

She listened, very patiently:
Then turned, when I had done,
To where a fine Forsythia
Was smiling in the sun.

Said she: 'I love this yellow stuff.'
And that, somehow, seemed praise enough.

Reginald Arkell

With an unlimited budget you can fill your toolshed with an armoury that would have made Henry VIII green with envy. There are peculiar poles with spikes on the end, or with rotating toothed wheels, that would have been far more effective than a simple halberd. Use them if you must. If you'd rather save money, then invest in a mere handful of the simplest tried and tested implements: A spade, a fork (the small border kind is especially useful), a rake, a Dutch hoe, a trowel, a pair of secateurs. These are the real essentials…

Alan Titchmarsh

Home-made
Jam

Apple
Wine.

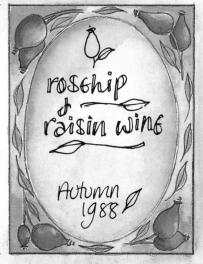

rosehip
&
raisin wine

Autumn
1988

Chamomile Tea

I propose ... to show, that, while, from a very small piece of ground, a large part of the food of a considerable family may be raised, the very act of raising it will be the best possible foundation of education of the children of the labourer; that it will teach them a great number of useful things, add greatly to their value when they go forth from their father's home, make them start in life with all possible advantages, and give them the best chance of leading happy lives.

William Cobbett,
from Cottage Economy, *1823*

Gulp
I loved my vegetable garden.
So here is my sad ballad:
I nurtured it for months
And ate it in one salad.

                                        Arnold Zarett

Even if something is left undone, everyone must take time to sit still and watch the leaves turn.

Elizabeth Lawrence

Look for a lovely thing
and you will find it,
It is not far –
It will never be far.

                                                  Sara Teasdale

If you truly love Nature,
you will find beauty everywhere.

                                                  Vincent van Gogh

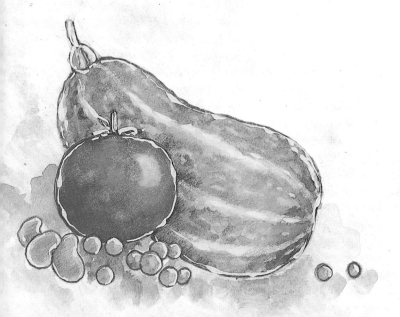

Onion sets: small onions planted in soil one day and transferred elsewhere by birds the next.
Rockery: what the builder left behind.
Self-sufficiency gardening: a method of growing vast supplies of the kinds of vegetables you would never normally eat.
Soft fruit: bird sanctuary.

Robin Clarke,
from the Completely Unillustrated Encyclopedia of Gardening

A Garden is the purest of human pleasures. It is the greatest refreshment to the spirits of man, without which buildings and palaces are but gross handiworks.

Francis Bacon

I believe a leaf of grass is no less than the journey-work of the stars.

Walt Whitman

One to rot and one to grow,
One for the pigeon, one for the crow.

Old English planting rhyme

* fennel *

· bay ·

· garlic ·

· sage ·

I like the smell of rotting leaves, especially walnut leaves, a nice clean aromatic smell; and I like the pungent smell of newly-turned earth; but most of all, I think I like the somehow nostalgic smell of a bonfire, never more than if it drifts in through an open window when I am snug in bed.

Valerie Finnis

A Forsaken Garden

In a coign of the cliff between lowland and highland.
At the sea-down's edge between windward and lee,
Walled round with rocks as an inland island,
The ghost of a garden fronts the sea.
A girdle of brushwood and thorn encloses
The steep square slope of the blossomless bed
Where the weeds that grew green from the graves of its roses
Now lie dead.

A.C. Swinburne

Use the time to muse over your successes and failures, and jot them down, lest you forget. Plants to order. Plants to ditch. Plants to move, and plants to give away to those who've been wise enough to admire them.

Alan Titchmarsh

What is a weed? A plant whose virtues have not yet been discovered.

Ralph Waldo Emerson

Bulb: potential flower buried in autumn, never to be seen again.
Carrot: a special food grown for carrot flies.
Drought: weather immediately following planting.
Green fingers: black finger nails.
Harden off: Kill by frost.
Hoeing: manual method of severing roots from stems of newly planted flowers and vegetables.

Henry Beard and Roy McKie
from Gardening: A Gardener's Dictionary

I don't know how people deal with their moods when they have no garden, raspberry patch or field to work in. You can take your angers, frustrations, bewilderments to the earth, working savagely, working up a sweat and an ache and a great weariness. The work rinses out the cup of your spirit, leaves it washed and clean and ready to be freshly filled with new hope. It is one of the reasons I am addicted to raspberry patches. The pie is purely symbolic.

Rachel Peden

I should like to inflame the whole world with my taste for gardens. It seems to me impossible for an evil-doer to share it.

Prince de Ligne

I'm still devoted to the garden ... although an old man, I am but a young gardener.

Thomas Jefferson